This book belongs to

....

....

Thank you for helping Buddy by protecting our rainforests!

For my husband and children who do so much behInd the scenes to help me share the message of these books - I couldn't do it without you! EJ

For Martyn. Thank you for your unwavering support and encouragement and for providing me with snacks when I am painting! LC

First published by Under Pressure Media Ltd
Looe Cornwall PL13 1HT

Text copyright © Eleanor Jackson 2019
Illustrations copyright © Laura Callwood 2019

Printed sustainably in the UK by www.exwhyzed.co.uk

10 9 8 7 6 5 4 3 2 1 0

A CIP catalogue record for this book is available from the British Library.

ISBN 978-1-9997485-5-5

To find out more about Buddy and the other Wild Tribe Heroes, plus teaching resources and how you can help, visit www.wildtribeheroes.com or Facebook, Instagram and Twitter @wildtribeheroes.

Buddy's Rainforest Rescue

Story by Ellie Jackson
Illustrations by Laura Callwood

Under Pressure Media Ltd - United Kingdom

The tangle of tall trees surrounding Buddy in the hot tropical rainforest were thick and green and teeming with life. He happily lived high in the treetops, spending his days searching for juicy ripe fruit and delicious sweet honey to eat.

He loved to swing from branch to branch, climbing higher and higher until finally resting in the tallest tree where he could see his magnificent rainforest home stretching out far beneath him.

One day, Buddy was reaching out and helping himself to his favourite fruit, with his hands and feet curled safely around the smooth bark of the tree, when suddenly he was interrupted by a horrible sound.

An awful cracking and splintering noise was getting louder and louder before stopping close by with a terrifying CRASH! Buddy felt his whole tree shake and tremble and his first instinct was to get away as fast as he could.

Quickly scrambling down, Buddy started grasping branches and vines, lurching from one tree to the next as he frantically tried to escape this frightening noise.

Feeling the familiar swinging sensation in his tummy, Buddy's fear calmed as he moved further away. Finally he slowed and stopped, resting a while before climbing up high once again only to see a strange and unnatural sight ahead.

Before him lay row upon row of short, oil palm trees, newly planted in straight lines, all the same size and all the same height.

Many of the insects and birds which normally surrounded Buddy had disappeared. Their chattering noise had been replaced by the constant drone of heavy machinery which steadily worked to cut down and clear away the ancient towering rainforest.

Sadly, Buddy realised he was far from home in this place he didn't recognise or understand, and as the afternoon rains started to fall, he knew he needed to find shelter.

Desperate to find a safe place, Buddy curled up in the canopy of the last tallest tree, listening to the heavy rains pattering around him. When the rains stopped he wove the leaves and branches together to make his nest for the night, before falling into an exhausted sleep, unaware of the noisy machines continuing their work below.

The cool morning air awakened him and looking down he saw a wasteland around the base of his tree; not a single leaf nor a plant, not an animal, insect or bird was left. Fallen trees surrounded him with their trunks and the life they contained upon them stripped bare.

Buddy stared in dread as a giant, dirty, spluttering beast whirred into life beneath him and started to clear a path through the ruined trees, ripping them apart and throwing them aside.

Anger now flooding his body, he clambered quickly down and raced along a fallen tree trunk, hopelessly trying to stop this thing from destroying his home.

The driver saw Buddy and instantly shut the machine down. At last an eerie silence fell around the desolate clearing, yet fear continued to haunt Buddy as he realised people were coming.

He climbed over the jumbled logs, stumbling and struggling to get away, not feeling the sharp sting that caught him on his side. Buddy slowed and gently fell to the ground in a deep sleep as the tranquiliser dart the vets had used, started to work.

The men working on the palm oil plantation had seen Buddy asleep in his tree that morning and had called the Orangutan Rescue Centre for help. The kind vets knew that Buddy would be scared and confused by the diggers and the noise. They also knew that they would have to move him to a new home, far away from the destruction caused by the machines.

As Buddy slept, the vets carefully placed him into a strong wooden crate in the back of their truck. They drove for several hours and it was almost dark before they safely arrived at the Rescue Centre where they gently checked him over before he woke up.

Buddy shook his head as the smell of fresh fruit reached his nostrils, slowly stretching his powerful body and feeling his strength returning. Venturing out into the cool moonlight, Buddy hungrily finished the fruit, leaves and honey which had been left out for him.

He heard other orangutans softly calling around him, and comforted by their presence, Buddy settled down to sleep, eager to meet his new friends in the morning.

As the sun rose, the rainforest burst into life with the noise of millions of insects, birds and animals. Buddy was eager to explore the large forest enclosure he found himself in. There was fresh fruit to eat, trees to climb, ropes and tyres to swing on and he enjoyed chasing and playing with his friends.

Many of the orangutans were very young and had lost their mothers, some had lost their homes like Buddy and some had been found injured or in people's homes as pets. All the orangutans were given a second chance at life at the Rescue Centre and the very lucky ones would be released back into the wild.

Finally the day came when Buddy was ready to be released deep into the rainforest where no machines would ever go. The people opened up the crates and one by one the orangutans climbed out and excitedly began to make their way towards the trees.

As soon as Buddy's crate was opened, he was off, climbing quickly up towards safety in the tall green rainforest, free from the machines that had cut down his trees, free to swoop and swing, to climb and to chase once again.

Did you know..?

There are three different types of orangutan and all species are endangered. This means that they could become extinct unless people protect them and their habitats.

Orangutans grow up to 1.5 metres tall - about the same height as a Year 7 student. They have a huge arm span - up to 2 metres, which is taller than most teachers!

Orangutans spend their time living in the trees and rarely come down to the ground. They make nests in the branches to keep them safe from predators such as leopards and tigers.

Their favourite food is a horribly stinky fruit called a durian which tastes a bit like sweet, cheesy garlic custard! They also eat leaves, bark, flowers, honey, insects and vines.

Orangutans are very flexible and can put their legs behind their heads. They are also very noisy making loud howls which can be heard for miles around. They have fairly long lives for a mammal - over 40 years!

Baby orangutans will stay with their mothers until they are about 10 years old. Their mother teaches them everything they need to know such as how to find food, make their nests and how to protect themselves. As adults they mostly like to live by themselves.

These beautiful animals are really clever and use tools such as sticks to scratch their backs, get insects out of trees or break open nuts. Some orangutans use big leaves to clean their faces or even make an umbrella to keep them dry!

Be a **Wild Tribe Hero** and help **protect** rainforests from being **destroyed!**

- Reduce. Buy only what you need and use less of what you buy. Stop using single use plastic such as plastic bags, straws and drinks bottles
- Reuse. Use things over and over again until they wear out
- Recycle your rubbish at home and at school. Lots of things can be remade into new products such as recycled paper
- Look for labels on foods that contain palm oil. Try to find alternative products that use sustainable palm oil or are palm oil free
- Consider supporting a charity that helps look after orangutans
- Tell other people about the problem of palm oil and deforestation and help spread the word by making posters and writing letters to save animals like Buddy

YOUR actions WILL make a difference!

Please share this book and its important message with your family, friends and teachers

What are the causes of deforestation?

Deforestation is the cutting down or burning of forests to clear the land to be used for something else. Reasons for deforestation are:

1. Growing crops such as palm oil and soybeans

2. Grazing land for animals such as cows for beef

3. Using the wood for buildings or furniture and to make paper

4. Building roads, towns and cities

What can be done?

Some countries now have projects to plant millions of trees to replace those that have been cut down. Reserves and national parks have been set up to protect large areas of rainforest from being destroyed. Local forest owners can be paid to look after their trees rather than to cut them down.

Wildlife corridors are a strip of natural habitat which can be left in plantations so that animals like orangutans can move between patches of rainforest and still have access to food, shelter and water.

Palm oil can be grown sustainably which means it is grown in a way that won't damage the planet. Companies need to make sure they are only using sustainable palm oil or use alternatives in all their products.

More Wild Tribe Heroes Adventures

Learning about the problems of ocean plastic

Duffy's Lucky Escape will transport you to a tropical paradise where Duffy the Sea Turtle lives amongst beautiful coral reefs and colourful fish only for Duffy to learn that not all that floats is food. As time is running out Duffy has a lucky escape when kind people step in to save the day.

Discovering the issues around balloon releases

Marli's Tangled Tale takes you to the cool and green cliffs where Marli the Puffin lives with her soon to hatch egg until one day the excitement of the far away town visits in an unexpected way. As hope starts to fade her tangled tale takes a twist just in time for the surprise waiting for her back at home!

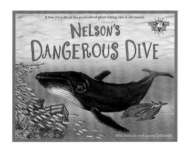

Exploring the issues around Ghost Fishing Nets

Nelson's Dangerous Dive goes deep underwater with Nelson the Whale where he discovers a hidden shipwreck and learns that what lurks below may not let you go. As he desperately signals for help, luck is on his side as a group of brave tourists give him the break he needs!

Join thousands of schools around the world who are using these books as a springboard into inspiring their children about environmental issues. We have a schools pack for educators to use in the classroom which supports the books combined with our online Teaching Resources where you can get free access to all online and digital resources – powerpoints, assembly scripts, curriculum links, lesson plans, teaching ideas, image gallery and more - www.wildtribeheroes.com

New Wild Tribe Heroes books OUT SOON!

How you can help Buddy and his friends!

One way you can help protect animals like orangutans is to write letters to companies who are contributing to the problem of deforestation and palm oil. When you are writing your letter always be polite and respectful as you are more likely to get listened to. Here is an example of one way you could write a letter. If you need more help please ask a grown up or teacher.

Dear Sir/Madam

I am writing to you about the problem of deforestation and palm oil in your products.

I have been learning about palm oil and how it is destroying our rainforests and harming our animals such as orangutans. Did you know that all species of orangutans are now endangered and will soon become extinct unless something is done to help them?

Please can you find alternatives to palm oil or use sustainable palm oil in all your products to help protect our planet and our future.

Yours faithfully

Wild Tribe Heroes